Descriptive Se

selected by Wend

Contents

LONGMAN

A British Playground

Cobwebs hung in the cold air,

Everywhere.

All around the playground,

They clothed the trees,

Dressed every bush

in veils of fine white lace.

Cobweb Morning

June Crebbin

2

A Jamaican Playground

The playground was slightly raised with the school in the background. The grass was worn away in places. There was a huge rainwater tank and a plot at the far corner, where the boys cultivated all types of vegetables. There were plum and apple trees scattered around. One area was reserved for playing cricket and another for volleyball.

from *Hope Leaves Jamaica*
Kate Elizabeth Ernest

A Storm in an Irish Field

Then evening slowly crept over the
    field,
Dragging its dark cloak over the sky,
Bringing the storm,
Lightning crackled brilliantly,
nightmare Christmas tree lights
Thunder was like the roar of an enraged
    beast
Filling my ears with a hissing rush
    of rain,
Icy, plump drops spattering the
grass, more liberal than the
    dew.

Milking
Avril Huston

5

An American Sunset

And the evening sun descending
Set the clouds on fire with redness,
Burned the broad sky, like a prairie,
Left upon the level water
One long track and trail of splendour,
Down whose stream, as down a river,
Westward, westward Hiawatha
Sailed into the fiery sunset,
Sailed into the purple vapours,
Sailed into the dusk of evening.

from *The Song of Hiawatha*
Henry Wadsworth Longfellow

The Seaside in Winter

There was no-one else walking along the esplanade. Only one or two of the street lamps were lit and in between the pools of light those threw onto the pavement were yards and yards of darkness, like rivers they had to plunge into ...

In summer along here, fairy lights were strung from the trees like the coloured glass beads of a necklace and music and voices came out of the hotels and people strolled up and down enjoying the warm evening air. But no-one came on a seaside holiday in December.

from *The Glass Angels*
Susan Hill

London in the Morning

This City now doth like a garment wear

The beauty of the morning: silent, bare,

Ships, towers, domes, theatres, and
temples lie

Open unto the fields, and to the sky,

All bright and glittering in the
smokeless air.

Upon Westminster Bridge
September 3, 1802

William Wordsworth

City Streets

Neon lights and take-aways
Gangs of boys and girls
Football crowds and market stalls
Taxi cabs and noise.

From the city cafes
On the smoky breeze
Smells of Indian cooking
Greek and Cantonese.

Out in the City
Gareth Owen

London at Christmas

And London shops on Christmas Eve
Are strung with silver bells and flowers
As hurrying clerks the City leave
To pigeon-haunted classic towers,
And marbled clouds go scudding by
The many-steepled London sky.

Christmas
John Betjeman

A Jamaican Christmas Market

The scent of roasted coffee beans and fried fish came from a nearby shop, bearing the sign 'Aunt Lulu's Diner'. But we didn't go there. We followed Grandma into the market-place, where the hagglers were already selling their wares.

Grandma stopped at a stall and admired the delicate pastel chiffon, satin and sequinned materials. Meanwhile, we children stared at Christmas decorations, balloons, coloured streamers and anything that appeared bright and shiny.

from *Hope Leaves Jamaica*
Kate Elizabeth Ernest

15

Snow in the City Streets

The house fronts looked black enough, and the windows blacker, contrasting with the smooth white sheet of snow upon the roofs, and with the dirtier snow upon the ground; which last deposit had been ploughed up in deep furrows by the heavy wheels of carts and wagons; furrows that crossed and recrossed each other hundreds of times where the great streets branched off; and made intricate channels, hard to trace, in the thick yellow mud and icy water. The sky was gloomy, and the shortest streets were choked up with a dingy mist, half thawed, half frozen, whose heavier particles descended in a shower of

sooty atoms, as if all the chimneys in Great Britain had, by one consent, caught fire, and were blazing away to their dear hearts' content.

from *A Christmas Carol*

Charles Dickens

A Country Mansion in the Snow

It was dusk – winter dusk. Snow lay white and shining over the pleated hills, and icicles hung from the forest trees. Snow lay piled on the dark road across Willoughby Wold ...

Snow lay thick, too, upon the roof of Willoughby Chase, the great house that stood on an open eminence in the heart of the wold. But for all that, the Chase looked an inviting home – a warm and welcoming stronghold. Its rosy herring-bone brick was bright and well cared for, its numerous turrets and battlements stood up sharp against the sky, and the crenellated balconies, corniced with snow, each held a golden square of window.

from *The Wolves of Willoughby Chase*

Joan Aiken

A Jamaican Church

On Sundays we attended the village church which was newly built. It was painted cream with columns supporting a porch. There was a cross on top and louvered windows reflecting in the sun. There were red poinciana trees blooming in the churchyard and the red blossoms littered the grass.

Inside the church, there were holy pictures on the walls, gas lamps hanging from varnished beams, fresh flowers, an altar, pews where the choir sat and a pulpit which was covered in a purple cloth. The wooden floor was polished regularly. As a result, several

parishioners had slipped while going up to take communion.

from *Hope Leaves Jamaica*
Kate Elizabeth Ernest

A Mosque in Delhi

By then they had reached the Jama Masjid, and went to sit on the sun-warmed stone steps. The mosque loomed behind them, one of the biggest in the land, its slim minarets piercing the sky, the marble dome full of perching pigeons. A long flight of red sandstone steps led up to the main door. People were going up to say their afternoon *namaaz*. The steps were also a place where hawkers sat selling their varied wares.

from *The House of Pigeons*
Subhadra Sengupta

A Miniature Sitting Room

Homily was proud of her sitting room: the walls had been papered with scraps of old letters out of waste paper baskets, and Homily had arranged the handwriting sideways in vertical stripes which ran from floor to ceiling. On the walls, repeated in various colours, hung several portraits of Queen Victoria as a girl: These were postage stamps, borrowed by Pod some years ago from the stamp-box on the desk in the morning room.

There was a lacquer trinket-box, padded inside and with the lid open, which they used as a settle; and that useful stand-by – a chest of drawers made of match-boxes. There was a round table with a red velvet cloth, which Pod had made from the wooden bottom of a pill-box supported on the carved pedestal of a knight from the chess-set ... The knight itself – its bust so to speak – was standing on a column in the corner, where it looked very fine, and lent that air to the room which only statuary can give.

from *The Borrowers*
Mary Norton

An Underground Home

And how ardently they grew to love their home under the ground; especially Wendy. It consisted of one large room, as all houses should do, with a floor in which you could dig if you wanted to go fishing, and in this floor grew stout mushrooms of a charming colour, which were used as stools.

from *Peter Pan*

J. M. Barrie

27

The Smells of Home

Whenever she opened Mrs McBride's front door, Tilly always paused, to stand on the inner mat and close her eyes and sniff in the special and particular smell of the flat. Most places had their own smell, their flat smelled of material, and sewing machine oil, the school hall smelled of polish and wood, her grandmother's house in Tenfield had smelled of coal smoke and smuts.

But Mrs McBride's smelled of – *what exactly*? Ginger biscuits, Tilly had finally decided. Ginger biscuits and violet-scented soap, mixed with a trace of candle-wax, a trace of silver-polish, a trace of horse-hair.

from *The Glass Angels*
Susan Hill

A Flat in Jerusalem

The best part of the flat was the balcony. You could sit there on a Friday evening, with all the work done, and look at the domes and towers and roofs of the grey and golden city spread around, and watch for the first stars to appear in the turquoise sky, and mark the end of the Sabbath.

On its balcony, there were cactus plants in squat red pots. In the days when you could buy cucumbers in the market, Aunt Pnina used to pickle them in salty water and leave them in the sun in tall, glass jars, where they floated in the milky, pale-green liquid like dead things ...

from *Golden Windows and Other Stories of Jerusalem*
Adele Geras

Hobbit Rooms

No going upstairs for the hobbit: bedrooms, bathrooms, cellars, pantries (lots of these), wardrobes (he had whole rooms devoted to clothes), kitchens, dining rooms, all were on the same floor, and indeed on the same passage. The best rooms were all on the left-hand side (going in), for these were the only ones to have windows, deep-set round windows looking over his garden.

from *The Hobbit*

J. R. R. Tolkien